THE RAGGY DOLLS

THE HOT AIR BALLOON

FROM AN ORIGINAL IDEA BY
MELVYN JACOBSON

ADAPTED BY
NEIL INNES

ILLUSTRATED BY
STEVE SMALLMAN

YORKSHIRE
TELEVISION

BOXTREE LTD

THE RAGGY DOLLS

The Raggy Dolls live in the Reject Bin in Mr Grimes's toy factory . . .

HI-FI was a talking doll, but when he was being tested, someone dropped him. He can still talk – but only with a stammer.

First published in Great Britain in 1990
By Boxtree Limited
Published in association with Yorkshire Television Limited

Text © Yorkshire Television 1990
Illustrations © Boxtree Limited 1990

The RAGGY DOLLS is a Trademark of Yorkshire Television Limited
© Melvyn Jacobson Productions Ltd

British Library Cataloguing in Publication Data
Innes, Neil
The hot air balloon.
I. Title II. Smallman, Steve III. Series
823'.914 [J]

ISBN 1-85283-044-1

Designed by Bet Ayer
Edited by Cheryl Brown
Typeset by Tradespools Limited, Frome, Somerset
Origination by Culvergraphics

For Boxtree Limited
36 Tavistock Street, London WC2E 7PB

BACK-TO-FRONT was a handy man doll with a complete tool-kit, but somehow the machine put his head on the wrong way round.

LUCY was sewn together with faulty thread. Now her joints are so loose, she goes to pieces if she gets excited.

DOTTY was perfect in every way – until she got splashed with paint that would not come off.

CLAUDE is a French doll. There is nothing wrong with him. He was part of a special export order to France, but the machine made one too many – and he was left behind.

PRINCESS should have had a tiara, beautiful hair, and a splendid dress – but the machine went wrong, dressed her in rags and cropped her hair.

SAD SACK was a sample, but because he was nice and plump, he used up too much stuffing. This made him expensive, so nobody wanted him.

One fine, sunny Saturday afternoon, the Raggy Dolls decided to go out to the big field, all except Sad Sack. He had made up his mind not to go with the others today because they always wanted to do things he wasn't much good at.

"Oh come on Sad Sack," said Dotty. "You can't stay in on a lovely day like today."

"I have made up my mind," said Sad Sack firmly.

"Don't be like zat, mon ami," said Claude. "We will do whatever you want to do."

"Except stay in!" added Dotty.

"My mind is made up," said Sad Sack, even more firmly.

"Oh well," said Lucy, "if you do change your mind, we'll be in the big field."

Sad Sack watched the others go. "Now, what shall I do?" he thought. "I know," he said out loud. "I'll change my mind!" And he set off to join the others.

There was no sign of the Raggy Dolls when Sad Sack got to the big field. "I wonder where they've got to," he thought.

Suddenly Lucy's voice came from nowhere. "Look, a lion!" she said.

"What? Where?" said Sad Sack, jumping back in amazement.

One by one the Raggy Dolls sat up. "Oh Sad Sack," said Lucy, "It's only a cloud.
Look up in the sky. . .see, it's shaped like a lion's face."
"Hi can see the face hof ha King," said Princess.
"Look, there's a jumping rabbit," said Back-to-Front.

Sad Sack sat down wearily. "You gave me a shock," he said. "I thought you'd seen a real lion."

The others began to laugh. Even Sad Sack raised a smile. He decided to join in.

Sad Sack lay on his back and looked up at the clouds. "It must be nice being a cloud, blown about by the wind," he thought. Suddenly he could see a face in the clouds – like a clown's, with a red nose that seemed to get bigger and bigger.

"I can see a clown with a red nose that gets bigger and bigger," said Sad Sack.

"Don't be silly," said Dotty. "How can a cloud have a red nose?"

"He's right though," said Lucy. "I can see a cloud with a big red nose too!"

The Raggy Dolls watched as the red nose got bigger and bigger.

"Th-that's n-n-not a n-nose," stammered Hi-Fi, pointing to the sky. "Th-that's a hot air b-b-balloon."

"And it's going to land in the big field," said Back-to-Front.

"Come on everyone," ordered Dotty. "Take cover."

The Raggy Dolls ran to the edge of the dark wood as the huge red balloon got nearer and nearer to the ground.

"Zut alors," said Claude, "eet ees going to crash!"

Luckily Claude was mistaken – the balloon made a perfect landing.

The Raggy Dolls watched from behind some trees as the man in the balloon worked the controls. He pulled a sort of string and flames shot out of a gas-burner, making a loud noise. The heat went up into the balloon and stopped it coming down too fast.

A boy with a bicycle who kept saying "Wow!" pedalled furiously into the big field.

"Wow!" said the boy as the man climbed out of his basket and quickly secured the big balloon with ropes and pegs and hooks.

"Good afternoon," said the man. "Can you keep an eye on all this while I telephone my ground crew?"

"Wow!" said the boy as the man hurried away.

The Raggy Dolls watched as the little boy became more and more curious.

"Oh no," said Dotty, "he's going to climb in. I'm sure the man didn't mean him to do that."

Suddenly a gust of wind caught the big balloon and two of
the pegs were torn from the ground.

The balloon was breaking loose!

"Raggy Dolls to the r-r-rescue!" stammered Hi-Fi.

The Raggy Dolls ran to catch hold of the ropes.
But it was no use, the balloon broke free and began
to lift off the ground.

The boy was thrown against the gas cylinder and hit his head, knocking him unconscious.

In no time at all, the Raggy Dolls scrambled up the rope and into the basket. Last of all was Sad Sack. "Oh dear, oh dear," he moaned. "Why did I change my mind – I'm no good at ballooning."

Lucy and Princess tried to make the boy comfortable.

"Hmm," said Dotty, "he needs to be in hospital."

"Yeah," said Back-to-Front, "but how are we going to get him there?"

"Don't look now," said Sad Sack gloomily, "but I think we're flying over the sea."

"Zut alors," said Claude, "Sad Sack ees correct!"

Hi-Fi spoke into his headphones. "Calling C-C-Coastguard, c-c-calling Coastguard. Boy injured. S-s-send help. Over."

"Well done Hi-Fi," said Dotty.

Meanwhile the balloon had lost height. Now it was only just above the waves.

"Pull ze string," shouted Claude.

"Right you are," said Back-to-Front. "No problem."

The gas burner roared and the balloon lifted, but not by much. Suddenly the flames stopped.

"We're out of gas," said Dotty, looking at the gauge.

"Oh no," thought Sad Sack, "I really don't like being blown about like a cloud in the wind."

"The wind is changing," yelled Dotty. "We're heading back towards land!"

"Yes, but there's a cliff straight ahead!" shouted Back-to-Front.

There was a bump and the balloon was soon tangled in the rocks and trees – halfway up a tall cliff.

"Here comes the Coastguard, take cover everybody," ordered Dotty.

The Raggy Dolls scrambled out of the basket and hid in some heather.

The boy opened his eyes. "Wow!" he said. "Where am I?"

The Raggy Dolls watched as the boy was rescued by a man on a long wire, dangling from a helicopter.

"Bravo," said Claude. "Now ee ees safe."

"Yes, but what about us?" said Lucy. "We're halfway up a cliff."

"Don't worry," said Dotty. "We'll be all right. We'll follow that rabbit path to the top."

The Raggy Dolls soon reached the top of the cliff. There, they found a car park where people could stop to admire the view.

"Look," said Dotty, "isn't that Mr Grimes's car?"

It was. Mr Grimes, the owner of the toy factory, had been out for an afternoon drive when he had seen the balloon crash. He'd parked his car to watch the rescue.

In no time at all, the Raggy Dolls had crept into the back of the car and were on their way back to the toy factory, hiding under Mr Grimes's jacket.

"I hope that boy's all right," whispered Lucy.

"I'm sure he is," said Dotty. "He's very lucky."

"Mais oui," said Claude, "eet could 'ave been worse!"

"W-w-worse for all of us," said Hi-Fi.

"Yes, but what han hadventure," whispered Princess.

"Yeah – terrific," agreed Back-to-Front.

Sad Sack couldn't make up his mind what to think.